Whoops!

Anne Adeney
Illustrated by Bernice Lum

Mike loved marbles.
He played with his marbles every day.

swirls

shooters

pearls

3

On Saturday, Mike played with his marbles in the living room.

Whoops!

"The living room is not the place for marbles!" said Grandpa.

On Sunday, Mike played with his marbles in the kitchen.
"The kitchen is not the place for marbles!" said Dad.

Whoops!

7

On Monday, Mike played with his marbles in the hall.

Whoops!

"The hall is not the place for marbles!"
said his sister.

On Tuesday, Mike played with his marbles in his bedroom.

Whoops!

"Not marbles again!" said Mum.

On Wednesday, Mum said, "Go outside and play with your marbles."

Mike played with his marbles in the garden.

On Thursday, there was a games
day at school.

Mike won all the marbles games.
"Not again!" said his friends.

His teacher gave him a prize.
It was a bag of marbles!
"Oh, no!" said everyone.